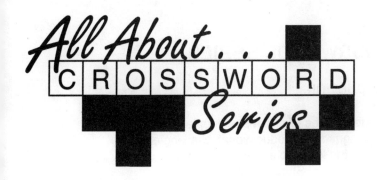

CW00741969

All About
COMPOSERS

CROSSWORDS by
DONALD MOORE

VOLUME IV

ISBN 0-89898-943-4

9 780898 989434

ALL ABOUT CROSSWORDS SERIES

INTRODUCTION

Crossword puzzles have long been a favorite pastime of millions of people. The ALL ABOUT CROSSWORDS SERIES is designed to be educational, challenging and entertaining. Your students will not only have fun learning about the world of music but also will learn about Language Arts, Social Studies and many other areas of the school curriculum. The puzzles can be integrated in a variety of ways, so use your imagination and, above all, enjoy them!

INCORPORATING THE ALL ABOUT CROSSWORDS SERIES IN YOUR CLASSROOM
Here are some suggestions for using the ALL ABOUT CROSSWORDS SERIES:

1. As an introduction to a topic or unit
2. As a conclusion to a topic or unit
3. As a supplement to a topic or unit
4. As a homework assignment
5. As an extra credit assignment
6. As an "emergency" classroom assignment for reserve or substitute teachers
7. As an aid in motivating "difficult" students in your classroom

NOTE: The ALL ABOUT CROSSWORDS SERIES can be introduced in your classroom with or without prior instruction about the topic. Since the ALL ABOUT CROSSWORDS SERIES involves other disciplines, the puzzles also may be used by other teachers not involved in the music program.

HOW TO SOLVE ALL ABOUT CROSSWORDS SERIES PUZZLES

It is suggested that you read the following instructions to your students before they attempt to solve the puzzles.

1. Begin the puzzle by reading the clues. Answer only the ones that you know for sure. Continue in the same manner until you have attempted all the clues. There probably will be several of them that you cannot answer on your first attempt.

2. Then take a moment and look at the entire puzzle. You will notice that parts of answers will have begun to appear in the puzzle.

3. Return to the beginning of the clues and attempt to answer the ones that you have not completed. Continue to refer to the letters and syllables that now appear in the puzzle. When thinking of an appropriate answer, consider the topic of the puzzle, various vowels and consonants that may fit in the blank spaces and other "clues" on the page that may help you obtain the correct answer.

4. When you have answered all the clues that you know, you may ask your teacher for assistance in completing the puzzle.

NOTE: Teachers may find it helpful to photocopy the appropriate word lists to assist students who may be less familiar with the material. You also may find that students enjoy working on the puzzles in groups of two to four people.

CONTENTS

1. ALL ABOUT JOHANN SEBASTIAN BACH

NAME: _____

PERIOD: _____

4

ACROSS CLUES

1. Smell, aroma
3. Bach was once a school _____
7. Lowers note 1/2 step or APARTMENT
10. 2nd syllable of the musical scale
12. Everyone has a big one
14. Santa sound
15. Johann Sebastian Bach, born March 12, 1685 in Eisenbach, _____
18. 6th syllable of the musical scale
19. Bach was a _____ musician most of his life or PLACE OF WORSHIP
21. Newspaper classified
22. Bach was an _____ at age 10 or CHILD WITHOUT PARENTS
23. Abbr. for DA CAPO (return to the beginning)
24. Bach's most notable music occupation
27. Singular of ARE
28. Period of time
29. Bach was a very religious _____ or ADULT MALE
30. Pronoun, thing
31. Bach was _____ in the last years of his life or TYPE OF WINDOW SHADE
34. 5th syllable of the musical scale
35. Abbr. for NATIONAL EDUCATION ASSN.
36. Abbr. for LARGE
37. Bach was a virtuoso _____
42. Supreme ruler
43. Every fisherman has one
45. Much of Bach's keyboard music was written for clavichord and _____
48. Bach's TWO and THREE _____ INVENTIONS written to teach keyboard skills or DIVISION OF HAIR
50. Bach famous organ work FUGUE IN G MINOR nicknamed "_____" FUGUE or SMALL
52. Payment for the use of property
53. Quarter, half or whole
55. Opposite of OFF
56. Spanish for YES
57. Used to soak up water

DOWN CLUES

1. Bach is most famous for his preludes and fugues for the _____
2. Document indicating ownership
3. Every child has a favorite one
4. Preposition
5. Red, blue, green or yellow
6. Homonym for HERE
7. Treble staff spaces
8. Sound of surprise, admiration
9. Bach's most famous organ work, THE _____ and FUGUE IN D MINOR
11. 4th syllable of the musical scale
13. Religious lady
16. Cow sound
17. Short sleep
19. Just below the mouth
20. Singular of HAVE
23. Past tense of DRY
24. Bach fathered 20 _____, 4 of them composers
25. Angry
26. Students love to _____ a pencil
31. Result of patting a baby's back
32. Abbr. for NO GRADE
33. Paul, John, Peter, James
34. Bach's AIR ON THE G _____
35. Bach used fast moving 16th _____ in his music for rhythmic vitality
37. Homonym for OAR
38. Abbr. for GENERAL STAFF
39. Abbr. for NO CREDIT
40. Abbr. for INTERNATIONAL HARVESTER
41. A wise man or lawmaker
44. Homonym for ORE
46. Homonym for ANNE
47. Abbr. for DOUBLE TIME
49. Postal abbr. for TENNESSEE
51. 7th syllable of the musical scale
54. Abbr. for EXTENDED PLAY

Solution p. 34

2. ALL ABOUT GEORGE FRIDERIC HANDEL

NAME: _____

PERIOD: _____

ACROSS CLUES

1. Santa sound
3. George Frideric Handel composed MESSIAH (1741) in 24 _____
8. Pulse in music
11. Oratorios differ from operas in that they have no scenery or _____
13. Handel lived during the _____ period
17. Abbr. for UNITED STATES
18. Alternate spelling for FERULE
20. Handel's MESSIAH is an example of an _____
23. Singular of ARE
24. Car horn sound
26. Popular car brand
28. Ceremony, celebration
31. Born February 23, 1685, died April 14, 1759 (last name)
33. Vegetarians hate this
34. Conceit, self-esteem
35. Handel's WATER _____ (1717)
36. Cheerleader yell
38. Abbr. for HOUR
39. _____, what, where and when
40. Two laughs
41. Yes, _____! or NAME FOR A FEMALE
42. Abbr. for OVERTIME
43. Handel lived for a brief time in this boot-shaped country
46. Handel's marital status
48. Slang for MOTHER
49. Postal abbr. for OHIO
50. Abbr. for EXEMPLI GRATIA (for example)
52. In 1726, Handel became a citizen of this English speaking country
56. Postal abbr. for NEW YORK
57. People do this when the HALLELUJAH CHORUS is performed
58. Handel attended _____ school or RULE
59. Handel's famous work, _____ (1741)

DOWN CLUES

1. Famous piece from MESSIAH, THE _____ CHORUS (1741)
2. Abbr. for OBERLIN COLLEGE
3. 1st syllable of the musical scale
4. Homonym for AN or PROPER FEMALE NAME
5. Abbr. for SOPRANO and ALTO
6. Homonym for SEW
7. 2nd syllable of the musical scale
9. In 1753, Handel lost his _____
10. Sticky substance used on roofs
12. 7th syllable of the musical scale
13. Short for BRADLEY
14. U.S. state, _____ ISLAND
15. SHHHHH!
16. Abbr. for UNITED SERVICE ORGANIZATION
18. Handel's ROYAL _____ MUSIC (1749) or EXPLOSIVES
19. Handel started to compose at age _____
20. Handel composed many _____ or PLAYS THAT ARE MOSTLY SUNG
21. Short for THOMAS
22. Abbr. for REPUBLICAN GOVERNORS ASSOCIATION
24. Both Handel and J.S. _____ were born in 1685
25. Short for EDWARD
27. Handel was born in this European country
29. Homonym for TWO
30. Abbr. for MORNING
31. Popular greeting
32. 6th syllable of the musical scale
37. Homonym for HANDEL
38. Popular meat from a hog
44. Past tense of TELL
45. To scream
47. Part of a camera
51. 4th syllable of the musical scale
53. Abbr. for GENERAL MOTORS
54. Adverb
55. Short for DIANA
56. Postal abbr. for NEW HAMPSHIRE

Solution p. 34

3. ALL ABOUT WOLFGANG AMADEUS MOZART

NAME: _____

PERIOD: _____

ACROSS CLUES

1. Wolfgang Amadeus Mozart was a _____ prodigy or KID
4. Mozart's father was his music _____
8. Large, enormous
10. Short for EDWARD
11. Lowers a note by 1/2 step
14. Short for AMPLIFIER
17. Haydn called Mozart the greatest _____ ever or MUSIC WRITER
20. 3rd syllable of the musical scale
21. Many teenagers have this disease
22. Mozart's native European country
24. Abbr. for POINT OF ZERO CHARGE
25. Mozart's opera, THE MAGIC _____ (1791) or WOODWIND
26. 1st syllable of the musical scale
28. Abbr. for RAILROAD
29. By way of, by means of
30. Close relative who guided Mozart's career
32. Mozart liked to play _____ or POOL
34. Slang for HOME RUN
35. Abbr. for OHIO UNIVERSITY
36. Abbr. for ONTARIO
37. Abbr. for POST SCRIPTUM
38. Mozart wrote his first symphony at the _____ of eight
39. Abbr. for LETTER OF OFFER
40. Mozart played several keyboard _____
48. Mozart's opera, DON _____ (1787)
49. Mozart had very little of this when he died
51. Abbr. for DA CAPO (return to the beginning)
52. Mozart's REQUIEM (1791) was finished by his _____, Franz Sussmayer or STUDENT
53. Most people like it when it's blue

Solution p. 34

DOWN CLUES

1. Abbr. for CENTRAL INTELLIGENCE AGENCY
2. Abbr. for POUND
3. People roll these in Las Vegas
4. Opposite of BOTTOM
5. Newspaper classifieds
6. Opposite of HIS
7. Theatrical production with singing, dancing and comedy
9. Green light
11. Homonym for FOUR
12. Mozart's middle name
13. 7th syllable of the musical scale
15. Mozart's _____ of FIGARO (1786) or WEDDING
16. Abbr. for PERSONAL COMPUTER
18. Born January 27, 1756, died December 5, 1791
19. Long, slippery, snake-like fish
22. Type of bomb
23. Abbr. for TO BE ANNOUNCED
24. Mozart wrote 17 _____ sonatas
25. Abbr. for FORTISSIMO (very loud)
27. Homonym for OAR
28. Abbr. for RHYTHM AND BLUES
29. Mozart played this string instrument
30. Only a few _____ attended Mozart's funeral
31. A rabbit does this
33. Vocal composition
41. Bottom of a window, door
42. Homonym for TWO
43. Abbr. for RECREATIONAL VEHICLE
44. Abbr. for UNIVERSITY OF ARIZONA
45. Postal abbr. for MINNESOTA
46. Short for NICHOLAS
47. Abbr. for BRIGHAM YOUNG UNIVERSITY
49. Yourself
50. Abbr. for EXTENDED PLAY

4. ALL ABOUT LUDWIG VAN BEETHOVEN

NAME: _____

PERIOD: _____

ACROSS CLUES

1. Homonym for STEAK
4. Ludwig van Beethoven's marital status
7. Beethoven played this keyboard
10. Abbr. for COMPANY
11. Short for DIANE
12. 3rd syllable of the musical scale
13. Beethoven's _____ Piano Sonata or LOVERS LIKE TO KISS BY THIS
17. People like to sing one of these
18. Joplin piano piece or OLD CLOTH
19. Born December 16, 1770, died March 26, 1827
20. To consume food
22. Pronoun, thing
23. Homonym for ADD or NEWSPAPER CLASSIFIED
25. Beethoven started to become _____ around the age of 30
28. Double reed woodwind instrument
29. Beethoven composed 32 piano _____
32. Smallest double digit number
33. Beethoven's _____ is the work of a genius
36. 7th syllable of the musical scale
37. 1/4 of a gallon
38. Opposite of HIS
39. Five lines and four spaces or FACULTY
42. Beethoven was born in this European country
43. Dog, cat or bird
44. Homonym for FOUR
45. Beethoven had a deep love for this close relative
48. Beethoven played this string instrument
50. Homonym for INN
51. Homonym for BEEN or STORAGE CONTAINER
52. Note without a stem or HOMONYM FOR HOLE
53. Green light
54. Beethoven's _____ in D or CATHOLIC CHURCH SERVICE

DOWN CLUES

1. Crust over sore during healing
2. Homonym for TWO
3. Homonym for NOT
4. Key _____ or YOUR NAME
5. Alternate spelling for NIGHT
6. Beethoven conducted his _____ public performance in 1824
7. Hog
8. Singers need this to sing or ATMOSPHERIC GAS
9. Beethoven played this keyboard with pipes (abbr.)
11. To pass away, expire
12. Postal abbr. for MINNESOTA
13. Honeydew or cantaloupe
14. The buckeye state
15. Quarter, half or whole
16. Abbr. for LEAVE
21. Half note gets two _____ ($\frac{4}{4}$)
24. Abbr. for DAL SEGNO (return to the sign)
25. Abbr. for DOWN
26. Preposition
27. Beethoven's first piano teacher
30. Quarter note gets _____ beat ($\frac{4}{4}$)
31. Spanish for YES
33. Abbr. for MAGAZINE
34. Beethoven composed 16 _____ quartets or VIOLIN, CELLO or BASS
35. Popular seafood or GRUMPY PERSON
37. Abbr. for QUICK-FIRING
38. Part of Beethoven's 9th Symphony is now a famous _____ or HOMONYM FOR HIM
39. Homonym for SEW
40. Three instrumentalists, singers
41. The number of Beethoven's most famous symphony
43. Ink loaded writing tools
44. Not very many
46. Abbr. for TO BE ANNOUNCED
47. Opposite of HERS
49. 6th syllable of the musical scale

Solution p. 34

5. ALL ABOUT STEPHEN FOSTER

NAME: _____

PERIOD: _____

ACROSS CLUES

1. Stephen Collins Foster abused this drink
7. Stephen Foster's music occupation
13. Abbr. for YEAR
14. Double reed woodwind instrument
15. Classical name for SONG
16. Abbr. for TRILL
17. Foster's _____ THE BANJO (1851) or JEWEL WORN ON FINGER
18. Abbr. for LIVING ROOM
19. Foster's GENTLE _____ (1856)
22. Abbr. for IN BOND
23. Pennsylvania birthplace of Foster
27. Abbr. for DA CAPO (return to the beginning)
28. Abbr. for KNOCKOUT
29. Born July 4, 1826, died January 13, 1864
30. Abbr. for MISTER
32. To chance or DANGER
35. Female fowl
36. Past tense of RUN
38. Short for RIO DE JANEIRO
39. Foster's OH! _____ (1848)
40. Abbr. for EMORY UNIVERSITY
41. Ghost sound
42. Postal abbr. for NEW YORK
43. Past tense of EAT
45. Abbr. for LIGHT
46. 6th syllable of the musical scale
47. Postal abbr. for GEORGIA
48. Some of Foster's artifacts are at the _____ of Pittsburgh
51. Group of instrumentalists
55. Postal abbr. for CALIFORNIA
56. Abbr. for INTRAVENOUS
57. Foster's JEANNIE WITH THE _____ BROWN HAIR (1854) or NOT HEAVY
60. Foster's early occupation
62. 3rd syllable of the musical scale
63. 24 hours
64. Favorite breakfast food
65. Barking sound of a small dog
66. Foster played this small woodwind

DOWN CLUES

2. Person who writes words to a song
3. Baby bed
4. Pigs
5. Abbr. for OBSTETRICS
6. Opposite of HIGH
7. Box, container
8. Homonym for OAR
9. The Christy _____ introduced many of Foster's songs
10. Slang for FATHER
11. One of 50 on the U.S. flag
12. Hallucinating during sleep
16. 7th syllable of the musical scale
18. State of being alive or MAGAZINE
20. Abbr. for NO GRADE
21. Postal abbr. for NEW HAMPSHIRE
24. Abbr. for TENSILE STRENGTH
25. Foster's _____ DREAMER (1864) or PRETTY
26. Vase used for ashes of the dead
27. Abbr. for DRIVE
28. Foster's MY OLD _____ HOME (1853)
31. Fee paid to composers, writers
33. Lawyers love this girl
34. Postal abbr. for KANSAS
35. Laughing sound
37. Abbr. for DEAD ON ARRIVAL
41. Foster's NELLIE _____ (1850)
44. Above normal body temperature
49. Abbr. for NATIONAL ART EDUCATION ASSOCIATION
50. Abbr. for VERY IMPORTANT PERSON
52. President Lincoln's first name
53. EGG _____, favorite holiday drink
54. Foster's OLD _____ TRAY (1853) or CANINE
57. To fib
58. Abbr. for GOOD
59. Cap
61. Abbr. for EXTENDED PLAY
62. Abbr. for MOUNTAIN

6. ALL ABOUT JOHN PHILIP SOUSA

NAME: _____

PERIOD: _____

ACROSS CLUES

1. Abbr. for MEZZO PIANO (medium soft)
2. 5 lines and 4 spaces or FACULTY
6. Infant
10. Present tense of SHOT
12. Abbr. for NATIONAL ASSOCIATION OF PROPERTY OWNERS
13. Sousa designed this instrument
15. Alternate spelling for John
16. Homonym for OAR
17. Favorite breakfast food
20. '60s song _____ OF EARL or PARTNER OF THE DUCHESS
21. Hockey players hit this object
23. Sousa's KING _____ MARCH (1897) or COOL FABRIC
26. Sousa's _____ POST MARCH (1889) or U.S. CAPITAL
29. Sousa wrote ten comic _____ or MUSICAL PLAYS
31. Abbr. for INTERNATIONAL BUSINESS MACHINES
32. To keep
34. Popular greeting
35. Popular weapon
37. People sit on this
38. Short horn sound
40. Eternity, endlessly
41. Conceit, self-esteem
43. 2nd syllable of the musical scale
45. Opposite of HERS
46. Homonym for ROLL
48. Sousa was director of the U.S. _____ Band or BRANCH OF SERVICE
50. Indicates silence in music
52. Homonym for INN
53. Sousa's _____ FIDELIS (1888)
54. Sousa's _____ toured the world

DOWN CLUES

1. Sousa made this with his band
2. People love to sing one of these
3. Everyone has a big one
4. Preposition
5. 4th syllable of the musical scale
6. Sousa, America's best-remembered _____ or CONDUCTOR
7. Abbr. for ASSOCIATED PRESS
8. Sousa wrote several novels and _____
9. Band concerts often begin with a Sousa _____
10. Opposite of HE
11. Pig
12. Opposite of YES
14. Born November 6, 1854, died March 6, 1932
18. 2,000 pounds
19. Slang for policeman
21. Slang for FATHER
22. Sousa is called "THE MARCH _____"
23. One of Sousa's music occupations
24. Opposite of BOTTOM
25. Not ever, no way
26. Sousa wore _____ gloves when conducting
27. Eli Whitney, inventor of the cotton _____ (1793)
28. Abbr. for TUBERCULOSIS
30. Abbr. for SOPRANO and ALTO
33. Sousa studied this string instrument
36. Sousa first played in the U.S. Marine Band when he was 13 ____ old
37. Sail the seven _____ or OCEANS
39. Abbr. for OVERTIME
40. Italian for THE END or DELICATE
42. Green light
44. Homonym for MAY or PROPER FEMALE NAME
45. Real cool or PART OF THE BODY
47. Coda or FINALE
48. Postal abbr. for MISSISSIPPI
49. Abbr. for ROOM
51. 7th syllable of the musical scale

Solution p. 35

7. ALL ABOUT SCOTT JOPLIN

NAME: _____

PERIOD: _____

ACROSS CLUES

1. Scott Joplin's music occupation
7. Joplin's parents were _____ or SERVANTS
12. 6th syllable of the musical scale
13. Quarter note gets _____ beat ($\frac{4}{4}$)
14. Kind of bread or WHEAT-LIKE PLANT
15. Every teacher has this
17. Divides measures or PIECE OF CANDY
19. Scott Joplin, "_____ OF RAGTIME"
20. Abbr. for RADIO FREQUENCY
21. Joplin taught himself to play this keyboard instrument
23. Popular army vehicle
25. Abbr. for AMERICAN LEAGUE
26. St. Louis, _____, birthplace of ragtime (state)
28. Short for LOUIS
29. To drink slowly
30. This bird gives a hoot
32. Past participle of SEE
34. Abbr. for SAINT
35. Postal abbr. for GEORGIA
36. Joplin's _____ LEAF RAG (1899)
40. Abbr. for EXTENDED PLAY
41. Abbr. for TRINITROTOLUENE (explosive)
42. Joplin rag "THE _____" (1902)
44. Abbr. for INTRAVENOUS
45. Abbr. for STRATEGIC AIR COMMAND
46. Abbr. for IDENTIFICATION
47. Abbr. for NO CREDIT
49. Joplin died in this famous east coast city (abbr.)
50. Homonym for INN
52. 1st syllable of the musical scale
53. Double reed woodwind instrument
55. Joplin died in a _____ hospital
57. Opposite of YES
58. Question of location
60. Eli Whitney, inventor of the cotton _____ (1793)

Solution p. 35

DOWN CLUES

1. Audiences _____ at the end of a musical performance
2. Abbr. for ON ACCOUNT
3. Blueprint, scheme
4. Homonym for SEW
5. Coda or FINALE
6. Abbr. for REGARDING
7. Chief characteristic of ragtime is _____
8. Longest body limb
9. Abbr. for VIDEO CASSETTE RECORDER
10. One of Santa's helpers
11. Abbr. for SOPRANO, ALTO
14. Postal abbr. for RHODE ISLAND
16. Homonym for SEA
17. Joplin's _____, THE RAG-TIME DANCE (1903)
18. Jelly ____ Morton (1885-1941), interpreter of Joplin's music or BUN
19. Act of affection
22. Postal abbr. for IOWA
23. Born November 24, 1869, died April 1, 1917
24. Strength, electricity
26. Joplin worked as a _____ in midwest clubs or PERFORMER
27. Signal, warning
31. Abbr. for LONG PLAY
32. 1973 movie that featured Joplin's music or BITE OF A BEE
33. Jealousy
36. Abbr. for MISTER
37. Past tense of EAT
38. Slang for FATHER
39. Audiences expect this at the end of a performance
42. Slang for former spouse
43. Short for EDWARD
45. To vocalize
48. Part of most woodwind mouthpieces or HOMONYM FOR READ
51. Abbr. for NATIONAL LEAGUE
54. Homonym for BEE
55. Yourself
56. 7th syllable of the musical scale
59. Santa sound

8. ALL ABOUT IRVING BERLIN

NAME: _____

PERIOD: _____

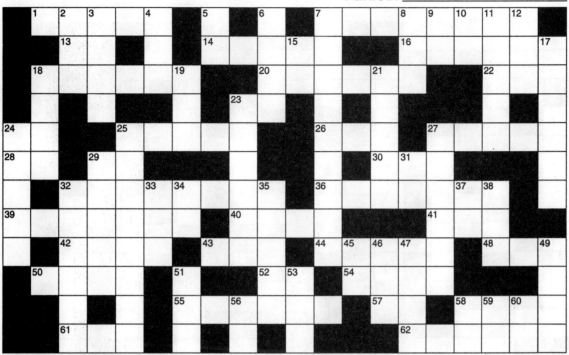

ACROSS CLUES

1. Irving Berlin could not read or write _____ notation
7. Berlin's occupation
13. Abbr. for SOPRANO and ALTO
14. Berlin's GOD BLESS AMERICA was sung by Kate _____ in 1938
16. First American native
18. Type of song written by Berlin
20. Berlin's EASTER _____ (1933)
22. Abbr. for GRADE POINT AVERAGE
23. Abbr. for BACHELOR OF SCIENCE
24. Postal abbr. for MINNESOTA
25. To accuse, fault
26. Homonym for SON
27. Everyone drinks this
28. Short for EDWARD
29. Abbr. for MARQUETTE UNIVERSITY
30. Period of time
32. Berlin wrote 19 Broadway _____
36. Berlin's OH HOW I HATE TO GET UP IN THE _____ (1942)
39. Berlin's GOD BLESS _____ (1938)
40. Des Moines, _____ (state)
41. Small child
42. Bowling alley, street
43. The movie HOLIDAY _____ (1942) featured Berlin's music or LODGE
44. Grin, happy face
48. Abbr. for OBBLIGATO
50. Famous singer NAT KING _____
52. Postal abbr. for GEORGIA
54. Berlin's GIVE ME YOUR TIRED, YOUR _____ (1949) or PENNILESS
55. Born Israel Baline, May 11, 1888, in this Soviet country
57. Abbr. for UNITED NATIONS
58. Comic strip character, LITTLE _____ or NICKNAME FOR LUELLA
61. Opposite of NO
62. Audiences usually demand this at the end of a performance

Solution p. 35

DOWN CLUES

2. Abbr. for UNITED STATES OF AMERICA
3. Homonym for SAIL
4. Abbr. for CENTRAL INTELLIGENCE AGENCY
5. Abbr. for DAL SEGNO (return to the sign)
6. Waiters and waitresses love these
7. Berlin's WHITE _____ (1942)
8. Boston Cream _____
9. Opposite of OFF
10. Abbr. for SPECIAL DELIVERY
11. Number of notes in a major scale
12. Type of rock music or TO TALK
15. Abbr. for TEACHING ASSISTANT
17. Opposite of WIDE
18. Berlin's ALEXANDER'S RAGTIME _____ (1911)
19. Abbr. for DEAD ON ARRIVAL
21. Coffee shop, lunch counter
23. Died September 22, 1989 (last name)
24. Berlin won a Congressional Gold _____ (1954) for his patriotic songs
25. Berlin's THERE'S NO BUSINESS LIKE SHOW _____ (1954)
27. Berlin's occupation from 1905-07
29. Painting on a wall
31. Abbr. for REGISTERED NURSE
32. Berlin's PLAY A SIMPLE _____ (1914)
33. Frozen water
34. Postal abbr. for CALIFORNIA
35. Berlin wrote 1500 popular _____
37. Opposite of YES
38. '60s Pontiac muscle car
45. Abbr. for MEZZO PIANO (med. soft)
46. Abbr. for I OWE YOU
47. Homonym for LOAN
49. Berlin's _____ SKIES (1927) or POPULAR COLOR
51. Abbr. for ORGAN
53. Everyone breathes this
56. Abbr. for SOCIAL SECURITY
58. Abbr. for LIBRARY OF CONGRESS
59. Abbr. for UNIVERSITY OF OREGON
60. Abbr. for LIVING ROOM

9. ALL ABOUT GEORGE GERSHWIN

NAME: _____

PERIOD: _____

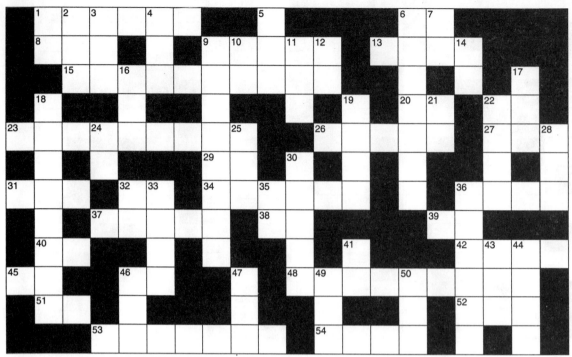

ACROSS CLUES

1. George Gershwin's I GOT _____ (1930) or ARRANGEMENT OF BEATS and ACCENTS
6. Slang for FATHER
8. Short for RIO DE JANEIRO
9. Gershwin was influenced by rhythm and _____ music or FORM OF JAZZ
13. Gershwin's musical OF THEE I _____ (1931) or CHOIRS DO THIS
15. Gershwin's _____ (from PORGY AND BESS, 1935) or HOTTEST SEASON OF THE YEAR
20. Postal abbr. for NEW HAMPSHIRE
22. Homonym for SEW
23. Gershwin died July 11, 1937 in this famous California city
26. Gershwin's AN AMERICAN IN _____ (1928) or FAMOUS FRENCH CITY
27. Opposite of NEW
29. Abbr. for KING OF ARMS
31. Monkey
32. Abbr. for ORANGE JUICE
34. Gershwin's brother, Ira, wrote these for many of George's songs
36. Quarter, half or whole
37. Gershwin's musical GIRL _____ (1930) or INSANE
38. Postal abbr. for CALIFORNIA
39. Abbr. for OAKLAND UNIVERSITY
40. Spanish for YES
42. Largest brass instrument
45. Yourself
46. "The Wizard of _____ "
48. Ferde Grofé arranged THE RHAPSODY IN BLUE (1924) for _____ and piano
51. 2nd syllable of the musical scale
52. Hotel, tavern
53. Gershwin was born September 26, 1898 in Brooklyn, ____ _____
54. Gershwin's symphonic jazz piece RHAPSODY IN _____

DOWN CLUES

1. Abbr. for RAILROAD
2. Opposite of HERS
3. Pronoun
4. Meat from hog
5. Abbr. for DRIVING UNDER THE INFLUENCE
6. Gershwin once worked as a jazz _____ or PIANO PLAYER
7. Homonym for ANN
9. Gershwin grew up in this New York city
10. Abbr. for LIEUTENANT
11. Abbr. for EMERGENCY MEDICAL TECHNICIAN
12. Abbr. for SOUTHEAST
14. Green light
16. Spring month
17. 5th syllable of the musical scale
18. Gershwin's music occupation
19. RHAPSODY IN BLUE was composed in just ten _____
21. Abbr. for HIGH SCHOOL
22. RHAPSODY IN BLUE was originally written as a piano _____ or ALONE
24. Abbr. for POUND
25. 24 hours
28. Homonym for DEW
30. Gershwin played this instrument
33. RHAPSODY IN BLUE is a combination of _____ and classical music
35. Abbr. for RED CROSS
36. Gershwin's I GOT PLENTY OF _____ (from PORGY AND BESS, 1935)
41. Abbr. for DA CAPO (return to the beginning)
43. Vase, coffee pot
44. Gershwin's musical STRIKE UP THE _____ (1930) or GROUP OF MUSICIANS
46. Quarter note gets ___ beat ($\frac{4}{4}$)
47. Homonym for FOUR
49. To steal
50. The night before Christmas

Solution p. 36

10. ALL ABOUT AARON COPLAND

NAME: _____

PERIOD: _____

ACROSS CLUES

4. Aaron Copland's book, WHAT TO LISTEN FOR IN _____ (1939)
8. Copland's _____ PORTRAIT (1942) or PRESIDENT FROM ILLINOIS
11. Copland was an _____ of several books
15. Opposite of SUBTRACT
16. Abbr. for ID EST (that is)
17. One of seven in a week
19. Copland studied music in this European country
21. Copland's LINCOLN PORTRAIT text is from the GETTYSBURG _____
23. 4th syllable of the musical scale
25. Opposite of YES
26. 1st syllable of the musical scale
27. Abbr. for DA CAPO (return to the beginning)
28. Abbr. for FORMULA WEIGHT
29. Percussion instrument or FOUND IN A CHURCH STEEPLE
30. Abbr. for MAELZEL'S METRONOME
32. To assist, aid
34. Abbr. for WEEK
35. One of Copland's music occupations
41. Homonym for BUY
42. Homonym for SEW
43. Born November 14, 1900, died December 2, 1990
48. Abbr. for ORGAN
50. Abbr. for CREDIT NOTE
51. To fall, descend
52. Homonym for AUNTS
53. Abbr. for DAL SEGNO (return to the sign)
54. Beethoven could not do this in his later years
55. Copland's ballet, BILLY THE _____ (1938) or YOUNG GOAT
56. 2nd syllable of the musical scale
57. Ghost sound
58. Abbr. for EXTENDED PLAY
62. Copland's ballet, APPALACHIAN _____ (1944) or SEASON OF THE YEAR

DOWN CLUES

1. Joins two notes of the same pitch or WORN AROUND THE NECK
2. Homonym for INN
3. Divides measures or PIECE OF CANDY
4. Abbr. for MEZZO FORTE (medium loud)
5. Short for SAXOPHONE
6. Abbr. for IDENTIFICATION
7. Abbr. for COMPACT DISC
8. Brass players need to keep this in shape or PART OF THE FACE
9. Automobile
10. Song title "THIS LAND IS YOUR _____"
12. Copland occupation or INSTRUCTOR
13. Opposite of EVEN
14. Not cooked much or VERY PRECIOUS
18. Ancient plural form of YOU
19. Copland used many _____ songs in his music or PEOPLE
20. Copland's FANFARE FOR THE _____ MAN (1942) or ORDINARY
22. Most people do this at night
23. Abbr. for FORTISSIMO (very loud)
24. Copland won many during his life
25. Copland was born and died in ___ ___ City
31. Abbr. for MEZZO PIANO (medium soft)
33. Copland played this keyboard
36. Copland won this award in 1949 for THE HEIRESS
37. Many cereals are made from these
38. Abbr. for SOPRANO and ALTO
39. Copland's ballet, _____ (1942) or COW ROPING CONTEST
40. Copland wrote eight film _____ or SPORTS TABULATIONS
44. Abbr. for NATIONAL RIFLE ASSOCIATION
45. Abbr. for OPUS
46. 6th syllable of the musical scale
47. Abbr. for NEW TESTAMENT
49. Supreme ruler
54. Rabbits do this
59. Abbr. for PIANISSIMO (very soft)
60. 3rd syllable of the musical scale
61. Abbr. for NO GRADE

Solution p. 36

11. ALL ABOUT LEONARD BERNSTEIN

NAME: _____

PERIOD: _____

ACROSS CLUES

1. Past tense of SHOOT
5. Opposite of EVEN
7. Abbr. for VOLTMETER
9. Leonard Bernstein song or THIS EVENING
12. Bernstein's ONE HAND, ONE _____(1957) or VITAL BODY ORGAN
14. Bernstein song _____ or IN A PLACE UNKNOWN
18. Corn on the _____
21. Abbr. for PIANISSIMO (very soft)
23. Homonym for ANN
24. Bernstein read this while conducting or SPORTS TABULATION
26. Bernstein recorded over 100 of these
30. Abbr. for GOOD CONDITION
32. Thomas Alva _____ , inventor of the first successful phonograph
33. Abbr. for ID EST (that is)
34. Body tissue
36. Increases value of note by 1/2
37. Born August 25, 1918, died October 14, 1990 (last name)
40. Jackson Five hit song or FIRST THREE LETTERS OF THE ALPHABET
42. Famous Bernstein musical based on ROMEO AND JULIET
43. Abbr. for DA CAPO (return to the beginning)
44. Popular adjective or GRAMMATICAL ARTICLE
45. Bernstein song I FEEL _____ (1957) or ATTRACTIVE
47. Coda or FINALE
50. Abbr. for REPUBLICAN GOVERNORS ASSOCIATION
52. Bernstein's instrument
53. Bernstein won this award twice
56. Bernstein was conductor of the New York Philharmonic _____
57. Abbr. for HORSEPOWER

DOWN CLUES

1. Two semi-tones OR PART OF A STAIRWAY
2. Santa sound
3. Quarter note gets ___ count ($\frac{4}{4}$)
4. 7th syllable of the musical scale
6. Homonym for DUE
7. One stanza or PART OF A POEM
8. Homonym for MAY or FEMALE PROPER NAME
10. Abbr. for HIGH SCHOOL
11. Homonym for TWO
12. Opposite of SHE
13. To throw, pitch
15. Slang for MOTHER
16. Most American speak this
17. Popular greeting
18. One of Bernstein's occupations
19. Homonym for OAR
20. Pulse in music
22. Slang for FATHER
25. Abbr. for COMPANY
27. Fibs, untruths
28. Sesame Street character
29. Bernstein book THE JOY OF _____ (1959)
31. Bernstein taught at the Berkshire Music _____ or MIDDLE
34. Shoes fit these
35. Bernstein attended this Ivy League university
37. Everyone is a human _____
38. Abbr. for NEW SERIES
39. Abbr. for TOUCHDOWN
41. Homonym for BUY
43. Nick, dinge
45. Apple and blueberry are 2 varieties of this favorite **dessert**
46. Small red spots on the skin
48. Abbr. for DOCTOR
49. One of two on the face
51. Opposite of STOP
52. Abbr. for DOCTOR OF PHILOSOPHY
54. Sound of surprise, admiration
55. Abbr. for MEZZO PIANO (medium soft)

Solution p. 36

12. ALL ABOUT JOHN LENNON AND PAUL McCARTNEY

NAME: _____

PERIOD: _____

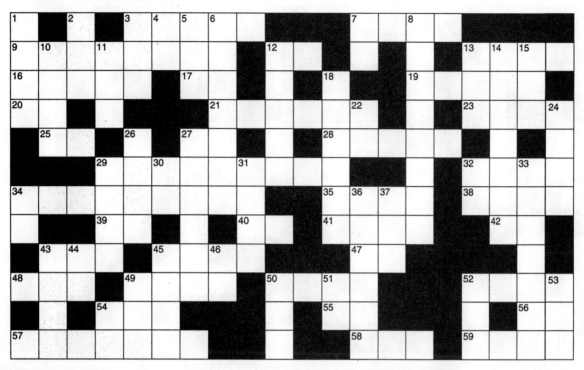

ACROSS CLUES

3. Humorous, comical or BROADWAY MUSICAL, _____ GIRL
7. John Lennon/Paul McCartney's _____ TOGETHER (1969) or MOVE
9. McCartney's LIVERPOOL ____ (1991) or LARGE CHORAL WORK
12. Homonym for BUY
13. Abbr. for YOUNG WOMEN'S CHRISTIAN ASSOCIATION
16. Tier of a cake
17. Abbr. for PARALLEL WITH
19. Young McCartney sang in the church _____
20. Abbr. for DA CAPO (return to the beginning)
21. McCartney plays bass left-_____
23. Abbr. for UNISON
25. Slang for former spouse
27. Abbr. for LEADING EDGE
28. Lennon/McCartney's SHE _____ YOU (1963)
29. Hometown of Lennon/McCartney
32. Ten cents
34. Born June 18, 1942
35. Shape of an egg
38. Finger click
39. Abbr. for NATIONAL LEAGUE
40. 6th syllable of the musical scale
41. Homonym for WEAR
42. Abbr. for GOOD
43. Short for JOSEPH
45. Lennon/McCartney's _____ ME DO (1964)
47. Abbr. for LIEUTENANT
48. Lennon/McCartney's WE CAN WORK IT _____ (1965)
49. Lennon/McCartney's I WANT TO HOLD YOUR _____ (1964)
50. Lennon/McCartney's IF I _____ (1964) or STUMBLED
52. McCartney's _____ ON THE RUN (1974) or GROUP OF INSTRUMENTALISTS
54. Household pet, feline
55. Lennon/McCartney's LET IT ____ (1970)
56. Abbr. for NOT AVAILABLE
57. Lennon/McCartney were members of this famous band
58. "She loves you, yah, yah, _____!"
59. Lennon/McCartney's THE LONG AND WINDING _____(1970)

Solution p. 36

DOWN CLUES

1. Lennon/McCartney had 42 _____ records (Beatles)
2. Lennon/McCartney's ____ TRIPPER (1965) or 24 HOURS
3. Homonym for FOUR
4. Alphabet letters for YOU ARE
5. Bite, pinch
6. Lennon/McCartney's _____ MAN (1966) or IN NO PLACE
7. Abbr. for COMPACT DISC
8. Famous Lennon/McCartney song or GIRL'S NAME
10. Indianapolis 500 mile _____
11. Lowest double digit number
12. Popular game or FAMOUS DOG NAME
13. Lennon/McCartney's ALL _____ NEED IS LOVE (1967) or HOMONYM FOR THE LETTER U
14. Lennon/McCartney's THE LONG AND _____ ROAD
15. Abbr. for CANCER RESEARCH INSTITUTE
18. Lennon/McCartney's _____ SUBMARINE (1966) or COLOR
22. 1st syllable of the musical scale
24. 2 semi-tones or PART OF STAIRWAY
26. Female person
27. Born October 9, 1940, died December 8, 1980
29. Lennon/McCartney's PENNY _____ (1967) or STREET
30. Postal abbr. for VERMONT
31. Andy Griffith Show's GOMER _____
32. Abbr. for DAL SEGNO (return to the sign)
33. Lennon/McCartney's LADY _____ (1968)
34. McCartney's _____ LOVE (1973) or BELONGING TO ME
36. Land between hills and mountains
37. Lennon attended the Liverpool School of _____ for 2 years
43. Lennon/McCartney's HEY _____ (1968)
44. Abbr. for OVERTIME
45. Opposite of EARLY
46. Abbr. for VAPOR DENSITY
49. Male proper first name
50. Beatle admirer or COOLING DEVICE
51. Abbr. for POUND
52. Divides measures or PIECE OF CANDY
53. Father
54. Abbr. for CENT

13. ALL ABOUT CAROLE KING

NAME: _____

PERIOD: _____

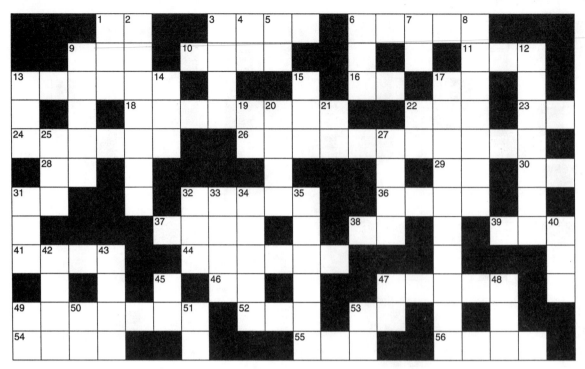

ACROSS CLUES

1. Abbr. for TEACHERS COLLEGE
3. Carole King loves to do this
6. King's A NATURAL _____ (1967) or FEMALE
9. Song title "Bye, Bye, Miss American ____"
10. King began singing at age _____
11. Abbr. for ET CETERA
13. King's YOU'VE GOT A _____ (1971) or PAL
16. Green light
17. Abbr. for COUNTRY & WESTERN
18. King's WILL YOU STILL LOVE ME _____? (1960) or DAY AFTER TODAY
22. King's ONE FINE _____ (1963) or PART OF THE WEEK
23. 6th syllable of the musical scale
24. High male voices
26. King was inducted into this hall of fame
28. Opposite of YES
29. Homonym for OAR
30. Short for EDWARD
31. Abbr. for POLICE DEPARTMENT
32. King started as a _____ songwriter or FIVE LINES AND FOUR SPACES
36. People do this on the phone
37. Most people find this in a box
38. Yourself
39. Resting place
41. Farmers put milk in this
44. King's TAPESTRY album (1971) won this award
46. Abbr. for EN ROUTE
47. King uses this when she performs
49. King's CHAINS (1962) was recorded by this all-time famous group from England
52. Abbr. for MISSISSIPPI STATE UNIVERSITY
53. Abbr. for OVERTIME
54. Short for KATHERINE
55. Short for SAXOPHONE
56. King's GO AWAY, LITTLE _____ (1962) or YOUNG WOMAN

Solution p. 37

DOWN CLUES

1. Joins two notes of the same pitch or WORN AROUND THE NECK
2. King performed for 70,000 people in _____ Park in New York City (1973)
3. Perform alone
4. Abbr. for INDIANA UNIVERSITY
5. Abbr. for NAVAL RESERVE
6. Dog tails do this
7. 3rd syllable of the musical scale
8. King wrote many of her hits in the Brill Building in _____ (city)
9. King plays this keyboard
12. King attended Queens _____, New York
13. Many adults think they are too _____
14. Abbr. for DISK OPERATING SYSTEM
15. Short for DOCTOR
17. Born Carole Klein, February 9, 1941
19. Abbr. for RAILROAD
20. King's UP ON THE _____ (1962) or TOP OF HOUSE
21. Abbr. for WEEK
22. Abbr. for DOCTOR OF DIVINITY
25. Coda or FINALE
27. Quarter, half or whole
31. Slang for SODA DRINK
32. To wilt, droop
33. One of four on a car
34. Most people hate to hear this in the morning
35. King is very _____ or WELL KNOWN
40. Homonym for DEW
42. Region, space
43. King's IT'S TOO _____ (1971) won best song of the year or TARDY
45. 2nd syllable of the musical scale
47. Postal abbr. for VERMONT
48. Human listening device
49. Abbr. for BOOK
50. Preposition
51. Spanish for YES
53. Steer or BIG, CLUMSY PERSON

14. ALL ABOUT TYPES OF COMPOSITIONS

NAME: _____

PERIOD: _____

ACROSS CLUES

1. Scott Joplin piano piece or OLD CLOTH
3. Instrumental composition with several movements
9. German song
12. Quarter note gets ____ beat ($\frac{4}{4}$)
13. Abbr. for REGISTERED NURSE
14. Part of an engine
16. Slang for person from Oklahoma
17. Religious song OR HOMONYM FOR HIM
19. Vocal composition with short movements, usually with instrumental accompaniment
21. Abbr. for AUDIO VISUAL
23. Drama set to music
24. This note gets 1/2 beat ($\frac{4}{4}$)
27. Homonym for INN
28. Abbr. for DA CAPO (return to the beginning)
29. Canon or CIRCULAR
31. To consume food
32. Ending, final passage of music
35. Abbr. for FEET
36. Type of jazz usually consisting of 12 measures
38. Air, tune
39. Abbr. for UNITED STATES NAVY
40. Abbr. for NOT AVAILABLE
41. Abbr. for MISTER
42. Abbr. for FORTISSIMO (very loud)
43. Homonym for OAR
44. Beethoven's FIFTH is an example
49. Composition for 3 instruments or voices
51. To sound again, repeat or TYPE OF COMPOSITIONAL DEVICE
53. Large choral work for soloists, chorus and orchestra
55. Abbr. for SOUTHBOUND
56. Religious lady
57. Smallest double digit number
58. Opposite of SHUT
59. To pull or TYPE OF BOAT

DOWN CLUES

1. 2nd syllable of the musical scale
2. Newspaper classified
3. Homonym for SUN
4. Opposite of OFF
5. Abbr. for NORTHEAST
6. Device to catch rodents
7. Homonym for AN or FEMALE PROPER NAME
8. Baseball tool
9. Short for LILLIAN
10. Abbr. for ID EST (that is)
11. Homonym for BUY
14. Abbr. for CIVIL AERONAUTICS ADMINISTRATION
15. John Philip Sousa composed this or MONTH
16. Orchestral introduction of an opera, musical comedy, etc.
18. Mongrel dog
19. Composition for solo instrument and full orchestra
20. Three note chord, group of three
22. Several music pieces joined together
25. Expression of wonder or $1000
26. Singular of HAVE
30. Abbr. for NORTHBOUND
33. Abbr. for OVERLAP
34. Famous actress, _____ Day
37. Round or HOMONYM FOR CANNON
38. Abbr. for MAELZEL'S METRONOME
40. Quarter, half, whole
42. _____ form, a composition not based on any music form or NO CHARGE
44. Vocal composition
45. Short for MONONUCLEOSIS
46. Abbr. for PAIR
47. Cap
48. Abbr. for YEAR
50. Double reed woodwind instrument
52. Household pet
54. Fluid for pen

Solution p. 37

15. ALL ABOUT CLASSIC FOLK IDIOM COMPOSERS

NAME: _____

PERIOD: _____

ACROSS CLUES

2. 3rd syllable of the musical scale
4. Postal abbr. for CALIFORNIA
6. Raises a note 1/2 step
8. John Jacob Niles (1892-1980), composer of I WONDER AS I _____ (1934) or TO STRAY
10. Jim Croce's (1943-1973) TIME IN A _____ (1973) or CONTAINER FOR LIQUID
13. Abbr. for INTELLIGENCE QUOTIENT
14. Woody Guthrie's (1912-1967) SO LONG IT'S BEEN GOOD TO KNOW ___ (1950)
15. Lawyers love this girl
16. Stephen Foster's (1826-64) OLD FOLKS AT _____ (1851) or HOUSE
18. Abbr. for EXECUTIVE OFFICER
19. Guthrie's THIS LAND IS YOUR _____ (1956)
20. 24 hours
21. Plural of IS
22. Opposite of GOOD
23. Abbr. for NEW YORK CITY
24. Abbr. for MORNING
25. Folk songs often tell a _____
27. Composers write music with this
28. 1st syllable of the musical scale
29. Bob Dylan (b. 1941) plays this reed instrument with his songs
33. To allow
34. Joan Baez (b. 1941), composer of _____ AND RUST (1975) or GEMS
40. Most houses have a front _____
41. Folk song themes are often social, sentimental or _____
44. Steer or BIG, CLUMSY PERSON
45. Opposite of OFF
46. James Taylor's (b. 1948) FIRE AND ____ (1970)
48. Everyone loves this season
52. Bob Dylan's BLOWIN' ___ THE WIND (1962) or HOMONYM FOR INN
53. John Denver's (b. 1943) ANNIE'S _____ (1974) or VOCAL COMPOSITION
54. Many folk songs have a verse and _____
55. 2nd syllable of the musical scale

DOWN CLUES

1. Short for ALLIGATOR
2. Postal abbr. for MINNESOTA
3. Thought, inspiration
4. Harry Chapin's (1942-1981) THE CAT'S IN THE _____ (1974) or BABY BED
5. Students should do this nightly
6. Abbr. for SOUTHEAST
7. Don McLean's (b. 1945) AMERICAN _____ (1971) or POPULAR DESSERT
8. Dylan was influenced by _____ Guthrie
9. Abbr. for AMERICAN UNIVERSITY
11. Abbr. for OLD STYLE
12. Crosby, Stills, Nash and Young's _____ YOUR CHILDREN (1970)
14. 365 days
16. Pete Seeger's (b. 1919) IF I HAD A _____ (1962) or CARPENTER'S TOOL
17. Yourself
22. _____ constrictor (snake)
23. Joni Mitchell's (b. 1943) BOTH SIDES _____ (1968) or AT THIS TIME
24. Woody Guthrie's son, _____ Guthrie
25. Folk songs are usually very _____ or EASY
26. Abbr. for TEACHERS COLLEGE
30. Abbr. for OVERTIME
31. Homonym for MADE
32. John Denver's TAKE ME HOME, COUNTRY ____ (1971)
34. Daniel Emmett (1815-1904), composer of _____ (1859) or THE SOUTH
35. Thing
36. Abbr. for MASTER OF CEREMONIES
37. Abbr. for NATIONAL LEAGUE
38. Choirs do this
39. Peter, Paul and _____ recorded many Dylan songs or HOMONYM FOR MERRY
42. Abbr. for LETTER OF OFFER
43. 7th syllable of the musical scale
45. Quarter note gets _____ beat (⁴⁄₄)
47. Postal abbr. for NORTH CAROLINA
48. Homonym for SEW
49. Alphabet letters for YOU ARE
50. Abbr. for MARQUETTE UNIVERSITY
51. Abbr. for MANUSCRIPT

Solution p. 37

16. ALL ABOUT CLASSIC JAZZ COMPOSERS

NAME: _____

PERIOD: _____

ACROSS CLUES

5. Type of jazz or NOT HOT
7. Group of musicians
10. Miles Davis (1926-1991) played this brass instrument
13. Short for MELVIN
14. To consume food
16. Postal abbr. for IOWA
17. Duke Ellington's (1899-1974) SATIN _____ (1958)
18. Type of jazz that originated in New Orleans
19. Household pet, feline
20. 7th syllable of the musical scale
21. Room for reading or BEAR HOME
22. Homonym for INN
23. Wild animals live at this place
25. Berklee School of Music, ____, MA
28. "The Wizard of _____"
29. _____ Corea (b. 1941) or YOUNG BIRD
33. Postal abbr. for WYOMING
34. Abbr. for ENLISTED MEN
36. Area around house
39. Postal abbr. for RHODE ISLAND
40. Not new
41. Postal abbr. for WISCONSIN
42. Miles Davis attended the Juilliard School of _____
43. Everybody likes this or NEEDED TO PURCHASE
46. 2nd syllable of the musical scale
48. Charlie Mingus (1922-1979) played this string instrument
50. _____ Carmichael's (1899-1981) STAR DUST (1929) or TYPE OF SANDWICH
51. Pronoun, thing
52. Fats Waller (1904-1943), composer of HONEYSUCKLE _____ (1929) or FLOWER
54. Abbr. for GOVERNMENT ISSUE
55. To publish, engrave
56. Every T.V. star wants this award
58. Popular woodwind used in jazz
59. W.C. Handy (1873-1958), composer of ST. _____ BLUES (1914) or MALE NAME
60. Abbr. for KENT STATE UNIVERSITY

Solution 37

DOWN CLUES

1. Jelly _____ Morton's (1885-1941) KING PORTER STOMP (1924) or BUN
2. 4th syllable of the musical scale
3. Abbr. for POINT
4. DOWN ____ Magazine or HOMONYM FOR BEET
5. String instrument
6. Duke Ellington's (1899-1974) SOPHISTICATED _____ (1933) or WOMAN
7. Receptacle for mail
8. Desire, want
9. Roy Rogers' wife or VALLEY
11. People listened to jazz on the _____ during the 1930s and '40s
12. Dave Brubeck keyboard instrument
13. Postal abbr. for MISSOURI
15. Bronzed skin
17. _____ Gillespie, (1917-1993), composer and trumpeter or DAZE
19. Kansas _____, birthplace of the swing style of the 1930s
24. Illinois city famous for jazz
26. Big band style of the 1930s
27. _____ Orleans, birthplace of jazz
29. Baby bed
30. To swear (slang)
31. Postal abbr. for KANSAS
32. Abbr. for POLICE DEPARTMENT
35. Errol Garner (1921-1977), composer of _____ (1954) or LIGHT RAIN
37. Abbr. for ROOM
38. ____ Ellington, composer of jazz
43. Thelonious ____ (1920-1982), jazz composer and developer of bop
44. Some cereals are made from these
45. Part of the face
47. Period of time
49. Abbr. for SOUTHERN ILLINOIS UNIVERSITY
50. Popular greeting
51. Contraction for I AM
53. Steer or BIG, CLUMSY PERSON
55. Abbr. for POST SCRIPTUM
57. 3rd syllable of the musical scale

17. ALL ABOUT CLASSIC COUNTRY COMPOSERS

NAME: _____

PERIOD: _____

ACROSS CLUES

1. Country _____, often called the only true American art form
4. Dolly Parton wears one
6. Don Gibson's (b. 1928) I CAN'T _____ LOVING YOU (1958) or TO HALT
9. Abbr. for MORNING
10. Soprano, alto, tenor and _____
12. Bill Monroe's (b. 1911) BLUE MOON OF _____ (1947) or BLUEGRASS STATE
17. Abbr. for LONG METER
19. Johnny Cash's (b. 1932) I _____ THE LINE (1956) or TO STRUT
20. Carl Perkins (b. 1932) BLUE SUEDE _____ (1956)
22. _____ Ole Opry or $1000
25. Abbr. for WEEK
27. Sluggish
28. Loretta Lynn's (b. 1940) COAL MINER'S _____ (1969) or RELATIVE
31. To move slowly or NASTY PERSON
32. Homonym for GUILDS
33. To possess
34. Yourself
35. Whole milk contains this
36. Abbr. for LEFT HAND
37. Hank Williams' (1923-53) I SAW THE _____ (1948) or BEACON
40. Night before Christmas
41. John Denver's (b. 1943) TAKE ME HOME, _____ ROADS (1971) or RURAL
42. This person sits behind the bar
45. Boudleaux and Felice Bryant's ROCKY _____ (1967) or PEAK
47. Abbr. for LONG PLAY
49. Jimmy Rodger's (1897-1933) T FOR _____ (1928) or 2ND LARGEST STATE
50. Short for WALTER
52. Buck Owens' (b. 1939) I GOT A _____ BY THE TAIL (1964) or LARGE WILD CAT
53. Hank Williams' YOUR CHEATIN' _____ (1952) or VITAL BODY ORGAN

DOWN CLUES

1. Tammy Wynette and Billy Sherrill's STAND BY YOUR ___ (1968) or MALE
2. Abbr. for UNIVERSITY OF MARYLAND
3. Abbr. for CITIZEN'S BAND (radio)
4. Famous Nashville AM radio station
5. Singular of ARE
7. Abbr. for OKAY
8. Church bench
11. In addition
13. Famous poet, Ogden ____, or ANTIQUE CAR BRAND
14. Abbr. for TOTAL LOSS
15. Abbr. for UNITED KINGDOM
16. Fred _____ (1897-1954), publisher of country music or FLOWER VARIETY
18. Gene Autry's (b. 1907) BACK IN THE _____ AGAIN (1939) or HORSE SEAT
20. Painful
21. Marty Robbins' (1925-1982) ___ ___ (1959) or TEXAS CITY
22. Instrument used in country music
23. Country Music Hall of Fame location
24. Abbr. for DUQUESNE UNIVERSITY
26. Roger Miller's (1936-1992) _____ OF THE ROAD (1964) or CZAR, RULER
29. Label, ticket
30. To decay
31. Abbr. for COUNTRY MUSIC ASSOCIATION
32. Postal abbr. for GEORGIA
35. Willie Nelson's (b. 1933) _____ HOW TIME SLIPS AWAY (1961) or AMUSING
38. Sick
39. Country music T.V. show, HEE ___
41. Abbr. for CERTIFIED PUBLIC ACCOUNTANT
43. Cartoon character, _____ Bear
44. Not cooked much
45. Short for THEODORE
46. Steer or BIG, CLUMSY PERSON
48. Tom T. Hall's (b. 1936) HARPER VALLEY _____ (1967)
51. Sound of amazement

Solution p. 38

18. ALL ABOUT CLASSIC BROADWAY COMPOSERS

NAME: _____

PERIOD: _____

ACROSS CLUES

1. Alphabet letters for YOU ARE
4. Meredith Willson's (1902-1984) THE MUSIC _____ (1957) or ADULT MALE
6. Richard Rodgers' (1902-1979) _____ PACIFIC (1949) or DIRECTION
8. The Broadway musical "The Wiz" is based on THE WIZARD OF ___
9. Andrew Lloyd Webber's (b. 1948) JESUS CHRIST _____ (1970)
14. Musicians listen with this
15. Andrew Lloyd Webber's _____ (1981) or FELINES
16. Abbr. for DISTRICT ATTORNEY
17. Abbr. for FIRE DEPARTMENT
19. Street name found in most cities
20. Richard Rodgers' _____ (1943) or SOUTHWESTERN STATE
24. Abbr. for RUNS BATTED IN
25. Abbr. for NATIONAL HOCKEY LEAGUE
27. Predecessor to musical comedy
29. Abbr. for AMERICAN LEAGUE
30. THE SOUND OF MUSIC (1959) is about the Trapp _____
32. Cole Porter's (1892-1964) _____ ME KATE (1948) or ACT OF AFFECTION
33. Victor Herbert's (1859-1924) BABES IN _____ (1903)
36. Present tense of BROUGHT
38. Quarter note gets _____ beat (⁴⁄₄)
42. George Gershwin's (1898-1937) GIRL _____ (1930) or INSANE
44. Opposite of DOWN
45. Postal abbr. for KENTUCKY
47. Frederick Loewe's (1910-1988) PAINT YOUR _____ (1951) or CART
49. Homonym for TEA
50. Stephen Sondheim's (b. 1930) A LITTLE ____ MUSIC (1973) or OPPOSITE OF DAY
51. Jerome Kern's (1885-1945) SHOW _____ (1927) or WATER VEHICLE

DOWN CLUES

1. Abbr. for UNITED STATES
2. FIDDLER ON THE _____ (1966), music by Jerry Bock (b. 1928)
3. Golfers do this on the green
4. Slang for MOTHER
5. Postal abbr. for ARKANSAS
7. _____, DOLLY! (1964) music by Jerry Herman (b. 1932)
8. Instrumental group that accompanies most musicals
9. Abbr. for SOPRANO and ALTO
10. Abbr. for POST SCRIPTUM
11. Jule Styne's (b. 1905) DO __ __ (1960) or MUSICAL SCALE SYLLABLES
12. 7th syllable of the musical scale
13. Actors usually do this in a musical comedy
15. Musical _____, a play with music
16. Short for DIANA
18. Frank Loesser's (1910-1969) GUYS AND _____ (1950) or KEN AND BARBIE
19. Richard Rodgers composed ____ with several lyricists
21. Abbr. for ASSOCIATED PRESS
22. Homonym for OAR
23. By, near
24. FINIAN'S _____ (1947) music by Burton Lane (b. 1912) or ARC
26. Galt MacDermot's (b. 1928) _____ (1968) or FOUND ON TOP OF HEAD
28. Homonym for PANE
31. George M. Cohan's (1878-1942) song, THE _____ DOODLE BOY (1904)
34. 6th syllable of the musical scale
35. Abbr. for DOCTOR
37. Irving Berlin's (1888-1989) ANNIE GET YOUR ____ (1946) or WEAPON
39. Part of the face
40. Smallest double digit number
41. Dog tails do this
42. To slice
43. Wild animals live in this place
46. Abbr. for OVERTIME
48. Opposite of STOP

Solution p. 38

19. ALL ABOUT CLASSIC ROCK COMPOSERS

NAME: _____

PERIOD: _____

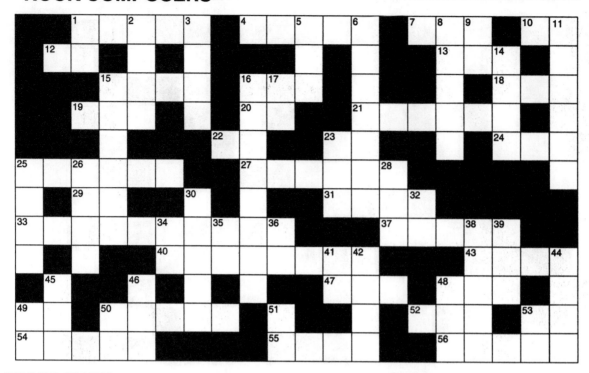

ACROSS CLUES

1. Roy Orbison's (1936-1988) OH, PRETTY _____ (1964) or ADULT FEMALE
4. Brian Wilson's (b. 1942) CALIFORNIA _____ (1965) or FEMALES
7. Abbr. for UNITED STATES OF AMERICA
10. Abbr. for POINT
12. Homonym for BUY
13. People get soaked in this or BATHING PLACE
15. No charge
16. Ray Charles' (b. 1930) WHAT'D I _____ (1959) or TO TELL
18. To possess
19. Bob Crewe and Bob Gaudio's BIG GIRLS DON'T ___ (1962) or TO WEEP
20. Opposite of DOWN
21. Chuck Berry's (b. 1926) ____ B. GOODE (1958) or NICKNAME FOR JOHN
22. Opposite of OFF
23. 1st syllable of the musical scale
24. Dion's (b. 1939) RUNAROUND ___ (1961)
25. _____ Richard (b. 1932) or TINY
27. Bobby Darin's (1936-1973) SPLISH _____ (1958) or SPLATTER
29. Preposition
31. 365 days
33. John Phillip's (b. 1945) _____ DREAMING (1966) or WESTERN STATE
37. Joey Dee's (b. 1940) PEPPERMINT _____ (1961) or TO TURN
40. Doc Pumus and Mort Schuman's A _____ IN LOVE (1959) or ADOLESCENT
43. Wilson Pickett's (b. 1941) IN THE MIDNIGHT ____ (1965) or 60 MINUTES
47. Jerry Leiber and Mike Stoller's HOUND _____ (1956) or CANINE
48. _____ and the Americans or BIRD VARIETY
49. Abbr. for GOVERNMENT ISSUE
50. Neil Sedaka plays this keyboard
52. To improvise with other instrumentalists or MARMALADE
53. Abbr. for DAL SEGNO (return to the sign)
54. Booker T. plays this keyboard
55. Otis Redding's (1941-1967) THE _____ OF THE BAY (1968) or PIER
56. Brian Wilson, one of the _____ Boys

DOWN CLUES

1. Postal abbr. for WYOMING
2. John Fogerty's (b. 1945) PROUD ____ (1969) or HOMONYM FOR MERRY
3. To want
5. ___ Charles, blind entertainer
6. Burt Bacharach's (b. 1928) DO YOU KNOW THE WAY TO ____ ____ (1967) or CALIFORNIA CITY
8. Jerry Leiber, Mike Stoller and Ben E. King's ____ BY ME (1961) or ENDURE
9. Abbr. for AMERICAN UNIVERSITY
11. Elvis Presley's (1935-1977) LOVE ME _____ (1956) or GENTLE
14. The Beach _____ or ADOLESCENT MALES
15. Little Richard's TUTTI _____ (1955)
16. Eric Clapton's (b. 1945) _____ OF YOUR LOVE (1968) or NATURAL LIGHT
17. Abbr. for ASSOCIATED PRESS
23. Buddy Holly's (1936-1959) THAT'LL BE THE ____ (1957) or 24 HOURS
25. Dogs like to do this to your face
26. Little Richard's LONG _____ SALLY (1956)
28. Cap
30. Booker T. Jones' (b.1944)_____ ONIONS (1962) or COLOR
32. Abbr. for RIGHT WORTHY
34. Abbr. for OVERTIME
35. Abbr. for NORTHEAST
36. Abbr. for ALCOHOLICS ANONYMOUS
38. Fats Domino's (b. 1928) AIN'T THAT A ____ (1955) or DISGRACE
39. Child's plaything
41. Short for EDWARD
42. Chuck Berry's ____ AND ROLL MUSIC (1957)
44. Small red spots on the skin
45. Melody or ATMOSPHERIC GAS
46. Cheap metal
48. To poke
49. Mick Jagger and Keith Richards' AS TEAR _____ BY (1964) or GREEN LIGHT
50. Slang for FATHER
51. Abbr. for ROAD
53. Abbr. for DA CAPO (return to the beginning)

Solution p. 38

20. ALL ABOUT CLASSIC MOTOWN COMPOSERS

NAME: _____

PERIOD: _____

ACROSS CLUES

1. Stevie _____ (b. 1950), composer and singer or TO BE CURIOUS
4. Berry Gordy, Jr. (b. 1929), Motown founder earned 367 million ____ in 16 years
10. Smokey Robinson's (b. 1940) THE ____ WHO REALLY LOVES YOU (1962) or QUARTER NOTE GETS ___ BEAT ($\frac{4}{4}$)
11. _____ Richie (b. 1950), composer and singer or MODEL TRAIN BRAND
12. Abbr. for NEW YORK CITY
14. Santa sound
15. Robinson, Richie, Gaye and Wonder, Motown _____ or CELESTIAL BODIES
17. Opposite of ALWAYS
20. Opposite of SHE
21. Abbr. for RIGHT
22. The buckeye state
24. Marvin ___ (1939-1984) Motown star
26. Name used for a group of Motown composers or ASSOCIATION
29. Abbr. for LOW WATER
31. Smokey _____, singer and composer
32. Abbr. for TURNPIKE
33. 2nd syllable of the musical scale
34. 4th syllable of the musical scale
35. One of the Three Stooges
36. Frosty is made of this
37. Abbr. for DEGREE
40. Abbr. for GREAT
41. Barrett Strong's (b. 1941) I HEARD IT THROUGH THE _____ (1966)
46. Holland-Dozier- _____ wrote most of Motown's early hits
49. Am, be, do, is, are, can or did
50. Short for EDWARD
52. Richie's _____ TIMES A LADY (1978)
54. Abbr. for ID EST (that is)
55. Once around the track
56. Robinson's GOING TO A __ - ___ (1965) or opposite of STOP-STOP
57. Gaye's DANCING IN THE _____ (1964)
58. Gordy's ____ BE THERE (1970) or CONTRACTION FOR "I WILL"

Solution p. 38

DOWN CLUES

1. Robinson's THE ____ YOU DO THE THINGS YOU DO (1964) or METHOD
2. Wonder's SHOO-BE-DOO-BE-DOO-DA-____ (1968) or ONE PART OF THE WEEK
3. One part of a tree
4. Midwest city where Motown began
5. 6th syllable of the musical scale
6. Short for ALAN
7. People do this in cars everyday
8. Hononym for SEW
9. ____ Gordy, Jr., founder of Motown Record Corp. or HOMONYM FOR BURY
13. Wonder's MY _____ AMOUR (1968)
15. Barrett _____, composer or POWERFUL
16. Robinson's _____ AROUND (1961)
18. Abbr. for VERY GOOD
19. To consume food
20. Bum or TYPE OF STEW
21. Diana ___, singer of Motown hits
23. Fluid for pen
25. One of Santa's helpers
26. Holland-Dozier-Holland's _____ SEE ABOUT ME (1964) or TO APPROACH
27. Abbr. for PROMISSORY NOTE
28. Added, additional
30. Holland-Dozier-Holland's HEAT ____(1963) or HAND MOTION
33. Robinson's GET _____ (1966) or BE PREPARED
37. Stevenson and Long's ____ WITH THE BLUE DRESS ON (1964) or DEMON
38. Night before Christmas
39. Robinson's MY _____ (1964) or FEMALE
41. Postal abbr. for GEORGIA
42. Abbr. for REGISTERED NURSE
43. Abbr. for NATIONAL BASKETBALL ASSOCIATION
44. Holland and Whitfield's AIN'T TOO PROUD TO ___ (1966) or TO PLEAD, ASK
45. Abbr. for INTERNAL REVENUE SERVICE
47. To fib
48. To allow
51. 1st syllable of the musical scale
52. Holland-Dozier-Holland's NOWHERE ___ RUN (1965)
53. Abbr. for ENTERTAINMENT TONIGHT

1. WORD LISTS: ALL ABOUT JOHANN SEBASTIAN BACH

Complete Word List

AD
AH
AN
AT
BLIND
BURP
CHILDREN
CHIN
CHURCH
COLOR
COMPOSER
DC
DEED
DRIED
DT
EP
ERA
FA
FACE
FLAT
GERMANY
GOD
GS
HARPSICHORD
HAS
HEAR
HO
IH
IS
IT
LA
LG
LITTLE
MAD

MAN
MOO
NAP
NC
NEA
NG
NOTE
NOTES
NUN
OAR
ODOR
ON
OR
ORGAN
ORGANIST
ORPHAN
PART
RE
RENT
ROD
SAINTS
SHARPEN
SI
SOL
SOLON
SPONGE
STRING
TEACHER
TI
TN
TOCCATA
TOE
TOY

Music Word List

BLIND
CHILDREN
CHURCH
COMPOSER
DC
FA
FACE
FLAT
GERMANY
HARPSICHORD
LA
LITTLE
MAN
NOTE
NOTES
ORGAN
ORGANIST
ORPHAN
PART
RE
SOL
STRING
TEACHER
TI
TOCCATA

2. WORD LISTS: ALL ABOUT GEORGE FRIDERIC HANDEL

Complete Word List

ACTION
AM
ANN
AS
BACH
BAROQUE
BEAT
BEEP
BRAD
DAYS
DI
DO
DODGE
ED
EG
EGO
ENGLAND
EYESIGHT
FA
FERRULE
FIREWORKS
GERMANY
GM
HAHA
HALLELUJAH
HAM
HANDEL
HANDLE
HI
HO
HR
IS
ITALY
LA

LAW
LENS
MA
MAM
MEAT
MESSIAH
MUSIC
NH
NY
OC
OH
OPERAS
ORATORIO
OT
QUIET
RAH
RE
RGA
RHODE
RITUAL
SA
SINGLE
SO
STAND
TAR
TEN
TI
TOLD
TOM
TOO
US
USO
WHO
YELL

Music Word List

ACTION
BACH
BAROQUE
BEAT
DAYS
DO
ENGLAND
EYESIGHT
FA
FIREWORKS
GERMANY
HALLELUJAH
HANDEL
HANDLE
ITALY
LA
LAW
MESSIAH
MUSIC
OPERAS
ORATORIO
RE
SA
SINGLE
STAND
TEN
TI

3. WORD LISTS: ALL ABOUT WOLFGANG AMADEUS MOZART

Complete Word List

ACNE
ADS
AGE
AMADEUS
AMP
ATOM
AUSTRIA
BIG
BILLIARDS
BYU
CHILD
CIA
COMPOSER
DC
DICE
DO
ED
EEL
EP
FATHER
FF
FLAT
FLUTE
FOR
FRIENDS
GIOVANNI
GO
HER
HOMER
HOPS
INSTRUMENTS

LB
LO
MARRIAGE
ME
MI
MN
MONEY
MOZART
NICK
ONT
OR
OU
PC
PIANO
PS
PUPIL
PZC
RB
REVUE
RR
RV
SILL
SKY
SONG
TBA
TEACHER
TI
TO
TOP
UA
VIA
VIOLIN

Music Word List

AGE
AMADEUS
AUSTRIA
BILLIARDS
CHILD
COMPOSER
DC
DO
FATHER
FF
FLAT
FLUTE
FRIENDS
GIOVANNI
INSTRUMENTS
MARRIAGE
MI
MONEY
MOZART
PIANO
PUPIL
RB
REVUE
SONG
TEACHER
TI
VIOLIN

4. WORD LISTS: ALL ABOUT LUDWIG VAN BEETHOVEN

Complete Word List

AD
AIR
AT
BEATS
BEETHOVEN
BIN
CO
CRAB
DEAF
DI
DIE
DN
DS
EAT
FATHER
FEW
FIVE
FOR
GERMANY
GO
HERS
HIS
HYMN
IN
IT
KNOT
LA
LAST
LV
MAG
MASS
MELON
MI
MN

MOONLIGHT
MOTHER
MUSIC
NITE
NOTE
OBOE
OHIO
ONE
ORG
PENS
PET
PIANO
PIG
QF
QUART
RAG
SCAB
SI
SIGNATURE
SINGLE
SO
SONATAS
SONG
STAFF
STAKE
STRING
TBA
TEN
TI
TO
TRIO
VIOLIN
WHOLE

Music Word List

AIR
BEATS
BEETHOVEN
DEAF
DS
FATHER
FIVE
GERMANY
HYMN
LA
LAST
MASS
MI
MOONLIGHT
MOTHER
MUSIC
NOTE
OBOE
ONE
ORG
PIANO
RAG
SIGNATURE
SINGLE
SONATAS
SONG
STAFF
STRING
TI
TRIO
VIOLIN
WHOLE

5. WORD LISTS: ALL ABOUT STEPHEN FOSTER

Complete Word List

ABE
ALCOHOL
ANNIE
ARIA
ATE
BAND
BEAUTIFUL
BLY
BOO
BOOKKEEPER
CA
CARTON
COMPOSER
CRIB
DAY
DC
DOA
DOG
DR
DREAMING
EGG
EP
EU
FEVER
FLUTE
FOSTER
GA
GD
HA
HAT
HEN
HOGS
IB
IV
KENTUCKY
KO

KS
LA
LIE
LIFE
LIGHT
LOW
LR
LT
LYRICIST
MI
MINSTRELS
MR
MT
NAEA
NG
NH
NOG
NY
OB
OBOE
OR
PA
PITTSBURGH
RAN
RING
RIO
RISK
ROYALTY
STAR
SUE
SUSANNA
TI
TR
TS
UNIVERSITY
URN

VIP
YAP
YR

Music Word List

ALCOHOL
ANNIE
ARIA
BAND
BEAUTIFUL
BLY
BOOKKEEPER
COMPOSER
DC
DOG
FLUTE
FOSTER
KENTUCKY
LA
LIGHT
LYRICIST
MI
MINSTRELS
OBOE
PITTSBURGH
RING
ROYALTY
SUSANNA
TI
TR
UNIVERSITY

6. WORD LISTS: ALL ABOUT JOHN PHILIP SOUSA

Complete Word List

AP
AT
BABY
BAND
BANDMASTER
BOOKS
COMPOSER
COP
COTTON
DUKE
EGG
EGO
END
FA
FINE
FOREVER
GIN
GO
GUN
HI
HIP
HIS
HOG
IBM
IN
JON
KING
MAE
MARCH
MARINE
MP
MS
MUSIC

NAPO
NEVER
NO
OPERAS
OR
OT
PA
PUCK
RE
REST
RM
ROLE
SA
SAVE
SEAS
SEAT
SEMPER
SHE
SHOOT
SONG
SOUSA
SOUSAPHONE
STAFF
TB
TI
TOE
TON
TOOT
TOP
VIOLIN
WASHINGTON
WHITE
YEARS

Music Word List

BAND
BANDMASTER
BOOKS
COMPOSER
COTTON
DUKE
END
FA
FINE
KING
MARCH
MARINE
MP
MUSIC
OPERAS
RE
REST
SA
SEMPER
SONG
SOUSA
SOUSAPHONE
STAFF
TI
TOOT
VIOLIN
WASHINGTON
WHITE
YEARS

7. WORD LISTS: ALL ABOUT SCOTT JOPLIN

Complete Word List

AL
ATE
BALLET
BAR
BE
CLAP
CLASS
COMPOSER
DO
ED
ELF
ENCORE
END
ENTERTAINER
ENVY
EP
EX
GA
GIN
HO
IA
ID
IN
IV
JEEP
JOPLIN
KING
KISS
LA
LEG
LOU
LP
MAPLE
ME

MENTAL
MISSOURI
MR
MUSICIAN
NC
NL
NO
NY
OA
OBOE
ONE
OWL
PA
PIANO
PLAN
POWER
RE
REED
RF
RI
ROLL
RYE
SA
SAC
SEE
SEEN
SIGN
SING
SIP
SLAVES
SO
ST
STING
SYNCOPATION

TI
TNT
VCR
WHERE

Music Word List

BALLET
BAR
CLAP
COMPOSER
DO
ENCORE
END
ENTERTAINER
JOPLIN
KING
LA
MAPLE
MENTAL
MISSOURI
MUSICIAN
NY
OBOE
ONE
PIANO
REED
ROLL
SA
SING
SLAVES
STING
SYNCOPATION
TI

8. WORD LISTS: ALL ABOUT IRVING BERLIN

Complete Word List

AIR
AMERICA
BALLAD
BAND
BERLIN
BLAME
BLUE
BS
BUSINESS
CA
CHRISTMAS
CIA
COLE
COMPOSER
DINER
DOA
DS
ED
EIGHT
ENCORE
ERA
GA
GPA
GTO
ICE
INDIAN
INN
IOU
IOWA
LANE
LC
LONE
LR
LULU
MEDAL

MELODY
MN
MORNING
MP
MU
MURAL
MUSIC
MUSICALS
NARROW
NO
OBB
ON
ORG
PARADE
PIE
POOR
RAP
RN
RUSSIA
SA
SALE
SD
SMILE
SMITH
SONGS
SS
SUN
TA
TIPS
TOT
UN
UO
USA
WAITER
WATER
YES

Music Word List

AMERICA
BALLAD
BAND
BERLIN
BLUE
BUSINESS
CHRISTMAS
COLE
COMPOSER
DS
EIGHT
ENCORE
INN
MEDAL
MELODY
MORNING
MP
MUSIC
MUSICALS
OBB
ORG
PARADE
POOR
RAP
RUSSIA
SA
SMITH
SONGS
WAITER

28

9. WORD LISTS: ALL ABOUT GEORGE GERSHWIN

Complete Word List

AN
APE
BAND
BLUE
BLUES
BROOKLYN
CA
COMPOSER
CRAZY
DAY
DAYS
DC
DUE
DUI
EMT
EVE
FOR
GO
HAM
HIS
HOLLYWOOD
HS
INN
JAZZ
KA
LB
LT
LYRICS
MAY
ME
NEWYORK
NH
NOTE
NUTTIN
OJ
OLD
ONE
OR
ORCHESTRA
OU
OZ
PA
PARIS
PIANIST
PIANO
RC
RE
RHYTHM
RIO
ROB
RR
SE
SI
SING
SO
SOL
SOLO
SUMMERTIME
TUBA
URN
YOU

Music Word List

BAND
BLUE
BLUES
BROOKLYN
COMPOSER
CRAZY
DAYS
DC
HOLLYWOOD
JAZZ
LYRICS
NEWYORK
NOTE
NUTTIN
ONE
ORCHESTRA
OZ
PARIS
PIANIST
PIANO
RE
RHYTHM
SING
SOL
SOLO
SUMMERTIME
TUBA

10. WORD LISTS: ALL ABOUT AARON COPLAND

Complete Word List

AARONCOPLAND
ADD
ADDRESS
ANTS
AUTHOR
AWARDS
BAR
BELL
BOO
BY
CAR
CD
CN
COMMON
COMPOSER
DAY
DC
DO
DROP
DS
EP
FA
FF
FOLK
FRANCE
FW
GOD
HEAR
HELP
HOP
ID
IE
IN
KID
LA
LAND
LINCOLN
LIP
MF
MI
MM
MP
MUSIC
NEWYORK
NG
NO
NRA
NT
OATS
ODD
OP
ORG
OSCAR
PIANO
PP
RARE
RE
RODEO
SA
SAX
SCORES
SLEEP
SO
SPRING
TEACHER
TIE
WK
YE

Music Word List

AARONCOPLAND
ADDRESS
AUTHOR
AWARDS
BAR
BELL
COMMON
COMPOSER
DC
DO
DS
FA
FF
FOLK
FRANCE
HEAR
KID
LA
LAND
LINCOLN
LIP
MF
MI
MM
MP
MUSIC
NEWYORK
ORG
OSCAR
PIANO
PP
RE
RODEO
SA
SAX
SCORES
SPRING
TEACHER
TIE

11. WORD LISTS: ALL ABOUT LEONARD BERNSTEIN

Complete Word List

ABC
AH
ALBUMS
AN
BEAT
BEING
BERNSTEIN
BERT
BY
CENTER
CO
COB
CONDUCTOR
DC
DENT
DEW
DOT
DR
EDISON
END
ENGLISH
EYE
FEET
FLESH
GC
GO
GRAMMY
HARVARD
HE
HEART
HI
HO
HP

HS
IE
LIES
MA
MAE
MP
MUSIC
NS
ODD
ONE
OR
ORCHESTRA
PA
PHD
PIANO
PIE
PP
PRETTY
RASH
RGA
SCORE
SHOT
SOMEWHERE
STEP
TD
THE
TI
TO
TONIGHT
TOSS
VERSE
VM
WESTSIDESTORY

Music Word List

ABC
ALBUMS
BEAT
BERNSTEIN
CENTER
CONDUCTOR
DC
DOT
EDISON
END
GRAMMY
HARVARD
HEART
MP
MUSIC
ONE
ORCHESTRA
PIANO
PP
PRETTY
SCORE
SOMEWHERE
STEP
TI
TONIGHT
VERSE
WESTSIDESTORY

12. WORD LISTS: ALL ABOUT JOHN LENNON AND PAUL McCARTNEY

Complete Word List

ART
BAND
BAR
BE
BEATLES
BINGO
BY
CAT
CD
CHOIR
COME
CRI
CT
DAD
DAY
DC
DIME
DO
DS
EX
FAN
FELL
FOR
FUNNY
GD
GIRL
GOLD
HAL
HAND
HANDED
JOE
JUDE
LA
LANE
LATE
LAYER
LB
LE

LENNON
LIVERPOOL
LOVE
LOVES
LT
MADONNA
MCCARTNEY
MICHELLE
MY
NA
NIP
NL
NOWHERE
ORATORIO
OT
OUT
OVAL
PW
PYLE
RACE
ROAD
SNAP
STEP
TEN
UNIS
UR
VALLEY
VD
VT
WARE
WINDING
YAH
YELLOW
YOU
YWCA

Music Word List

ART
BAND
BAR
BE
BEATLES
CHOIR
COME
DAY
DC
DO
DS
FAN
FELL
FUNNY
GOLD
HAND
HANDED
JUDE
LA
LANE
LENNON
LIVERPOOL
LOVE
LOVES
MADONNA
MCCARTNEY
MICHELLE
MY
NOWHERE
ORATORIO
OUT
ROAD
STEP
UNIS
WINDING
YAH
YELLOW
YOU

13. WORD LISTS: ALL CAROLE KING

Complete Word List

ALARM
AREA
AT
BEATLES
BED
BK
CAROLEKING
CENTRAL
COLLEGE
CW
DAY
DD
DOC
DOS
DUE
EAR
ED
END
ER
ETC
FAMOUS
FAT
FOUR
FRIEND
GIRL
GO
GRAMMY
IU
KATE
LA
LATE
MAIL
ME
MI

MSU
NEWYORK
NO
NOTE
NR
OR
OT
OX
PAIL
PD
PIANO
PIE
POP
RE
ROCKANDROLL
ROOF
RR
SAG
SAX
SI
SING
SOLO
STAFF
TALK
TC
TENORS
TIE
TIRE
TOMORROW
VOICE
VT
WAG
WK
WOMAN

Music Word List

BEATLES
CAROLEKING
CENTRAL
COLLEGE
CW
DAY
END
FAMOUS
FOUR
FRIEND
GIRL
GRAMMY
LA
LATE
MI
NEWYORK
NOTE
PIANO
PIE
RE
ROCKANDROLL
ROOF
SAX
SING
SOLO
STAFF
TENORS
TIE
TOMORROW
VOICE
WOMAN

14. WORD LISTS: ALL ABOUT TYPES OF COMPOSITIONS

Complete Word List

AD
ANNE
AV
BAT
BLUES
BY
CAA
CAM
CANON
CANTATA
CAT
CODA
CONCERTO
DC
DORIS
EAT
ECHO
EIGHTH
FF
FREE
FT
GEE
HAS
HAT
HYMN
IE
IN
INK
LIED
LIL
MARCH
MEDLEY
MELODY
MM
MONO

MR
MUTT
NA
NB
NE
NOTES
NUN
OBOE
OKIE
OL
ON
ONE
OPEN
OPERA
OR
ORATORIO
OVERTURE
PR
RAG
RE
RN
ROUND
SB
SON
SONATA
SONG
SYMPHONY
TEN
TRAP
TRAID
TRIO
TUG
USN
YR

Music Word List

BLUES
CANON
CANTATA
CODA
CONCERTO
DC
ECHO
EIGHTH
FF
FREE
HYMN
LIED
MARCH
MEDLEY
MELODY
MM
NOTES
OBOE
ONE
OPERA
ORATORIO
OVERTURE
RAG
RE
ROUND
SONATA
SONG
SYMPHONY
TRIAD
TRIO

15. WORD LISTS: ALL ABOUT CLASSIC FOLK IDIOM COMPOSERS

Complete Word List

AM
ARE
ARLO
AU
BAD
BOA
BOTTLE
CA
CHORUS
CRADLE
DAY
DIAMONDS
DIXIE
DO
DOOR
EO
GATOR
HAMMER
HARMONICA
HOME
IDEA
IN
IQ
IT
LAND
LET
LO
MAID
MARY
MC
ME
MI
MN
MS

MU
NC
NL
NOW
NYC
ON
ONE
OS
OT
OX
PEN
PIE
POLITICAL
RAIN
RE
ROADS
SE
SHARP
SIMPLE
SING
SONG
SO
STORY
STUDY
SUE
SUMMER
TC
TEACH
TI
UR
WANDER
WOODY
YEAR
YOU

Music Word List

ARLO
BOTTLE
CHORUS
CRADLE
DIAMONDS
DIXIE
DO
HAMMER
HARMONICA
HOME
LAND
MARY
MI
NOW
ONE
PEN
PIE
POLITICAL
RAIN
RE
ROADS
SHARP
SIMPLE
SING
SONG
STORY
TEACH
TI
WANDER
WOODY
YOU

16. WORD LISTS: ALL ABOUT CLASSIC JAZZ COMPOSERS

Complete Word List

BAND
BASS
BEAT
BOSTON
BOX
CAT
CELLO
CHICAGO
CHICK
CITY
COOL
CRIB
CUSS
DALE
DEN
DIXIELAND
DIZZY
DOLL
DUKE
EAT
EM
EMMY
ERA
EYE
FA
GI
HI
HOAGY
IA
IM
IN
IT
KS
KSU
LADY

LOUIS
MEL
MI
MISTY
MO
MONEY
MONK
MUSIC
NEED
NEW
OATS
OX
OZ
PD
PIANO
PRINT
PS
PT
RADIO
RE
RI
RM
ROLL
ROSE
SAX
SIU
SWING
TAN
TI
TRUMPET
USED
WI
WY
YARD
ZOO

Music Word List

BAND
BASS
BEAT
BOSTON
CELLO
CHICAGO
CHICK
CITY
COOL
DIXIELAND
DIZZY
DOLL
DUKE
FA
HOAGY
LADY
LOUIS
MI
MISTY
MONK
MUSIC
NEW
PIANO
RADIO
RE
ROLL
ROSE
SAX
SWING
TI
TRUMPET

17. WORD LISTS: ALL ABOUT CLASSIC COUNTRY COMPOSERS

Complete Word List

AH
ALSO
AM
BASS
CB
CMA
COUNTRY
CPA
CREEP
DAUGHTER
DU
ELPASO
EVE
FAT
FUNNY
GA
GILDS
GRAND
GUITAR
HAW
HEART
ILL
IS
KENTUCKY
KING
LAWYER
LH
LIGHT
LM
LP
MAN

ME
MUSIC
NASH
NASHVILLE
OK
OWN
OX
PEW
PTA
RARE
ROSE
ROT
SADDLE
SHOES
SLOW
SORE
STOP
TAG
TED
TEXAS
TIGER
TL
TOP
UK
UM
WALK
WALT
WIG
WK
WSM
YOGI

Music Word List

BASS
CMA
COUNTRY
DAUGHTER
ELPASO
FUNNY
GRAND
GUITAR
HAW
HEART
KENTUCKY
KING
LIGHT
LM
MAN
MUSIC
NASHVILLE
PTA
ROSE
SADDLE
SHOES
STOP
TEXAS
TIGER
TOP
WALK
WIG
WSM

18. WORD LISTS: ALL ABOUT CLASSIC BROADWAY COMPOSERS

Complete Word List

AL
AP
AR
AT
BOAT
BRING
CATS
COMEDY
CRAZY
CUT
DA
DANCE
DI
DOLLS
DR
EAR
EYE
FAMILY
FD
GO
GUN
HAIR
HELLO
KISS
KY
LA
MA
MAIN
MAN
MUSIC
NHL
NIGHT
OKLAHOMA

ONE
OPERETTA
OR
ORCHESTRA
OT
OZ
PAIN
PS
PUTT
RAINBOW
RBI
REMI
ROOF
SA
SOUTH
SUPERSTAR
TEE
TEN
TI
TOYLAND
UP
UR
US
WAG
WAGON
YANKEE
ZOO

Music Word List

BOAT
CATS
COMEDY
CRAZY
DANCE
DOLLS
EAR
FAMILY
GUN
HAIR
HELLO
KISS
LA
MAN
MUSIC
NIGHT
OKLAHOMA
ONE
OPERETTA
ORCHESTRA
OZ
RAINBOW
REMI
ROOF
SA
SOUTH
SUPERSTAR
TI
TOYLAND
WAGON
YANKEE

19. WORD LISTS: ALL ABOUT CLASSIC ROCK COMPOSERS

Complete Word List

AA
AIR
AP
AT
AU
BEACH
BOYS
BY
CALIFORNIA
CRY
DAY
DC
DO
DOCK
DOG
DS
ED
FREE
FRUTTI
GI
GIRLS
GO
GREEN
HAT
HOUR
JAB
JAM
JAY
JOHNNY
LICK
LITTLE
MARY
NE
NEED
ON

ORGAN
OT
OWN
PA
PIANO
PT
RASH
RAY
RD
ROCK
RW
SANJOSE
SAY
SHAME
SPLASH
STAND
SUE
SUNSHINE
TALL
TEENAGER
TENDER
TIN
TOY
TUB
TWIST
UP
USA
WOMAN
WY
YEAR

Music Word List

AIR
BEACH

BOYS
CALIFORNIA
CRY
DAY
DC
DO
DOCK
DOG
DS
FRUTTI
GIRLS
GO
GREEN
HOUR
JAM
JAY
JOHNNY
LITTLE
MARY
ORGAN
PIANO
RAY
ROCK
SANJOSE
SAY
SHAME
SPLASH
STAND
SUE
SUNSHINE
TALL
TEENAGER
TENDER
TWIST
WOMAN

20. WORD LISTS: ALL ABOUT CLASSIC MOTOWN COMPOSERS

Complete Word List

AL
ANOTHER
BEG
BERRY
CHERIE
COME
CORPORATION
DAY
DEG
DEVIL
DETROIT
DO
DOLLARS
EAT
ED
ELF
ET
EVE
FA
GA
GAYE
GIRL
GOGO
GRAPEVINE
GT
HE
HO
HOBO
HOLLAND
IE
ILL
INK
IRS
LA
LAP

LET
LIE
LIONEL
LW
MOE
NBA
NEVER
NYC
OHIO
ONE
PN
RE
READY
RIDE
RN
ROBINSON
ROOT
ROSS
RT
SHOP
SNOW
SO
STARS
STREET
STRONG
THREE
TO
TPK
VERB
VG
WAVE
WAY
WONDER

Music Word List

BEG
BERRY
CHERIE
COME
CORPORATION
DAY
DETROIT
DEVIL
DO
DOLLARS
FA
GAYE
GIRL
GOGO
GRAPEVINE
HOLLAND
ILL
LA
LIONEL
ONE
RE
READY
ROBINSON
ROSS
SHOP
STARS
STREET
STRONG
THREE
TO
WAVE
WAY
WONDER

SOLUTIONS

1. ALL ABOUT JOHANN SEBASTIAN BACH

2. ALL ABOUT GEORGE FRIDERIC HANDEL

3. ALL ABOUT WOLFGANG AMADEUS MOZART

4. ALL ABOUT LUDWIG VAN BEETHOVEN

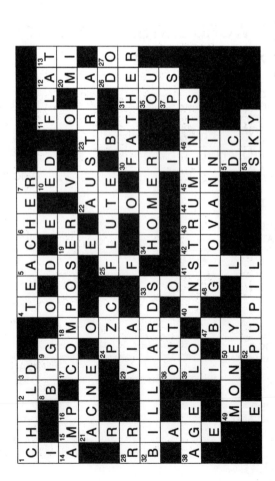

SOLUTIONS

5. ALL ABOUT STEPHEN FOSTER

6. ALL ABOUT JOHN PHILIP SOUSA

7. ALL ABOUT SCOTT JOPLIN

8. ALL ABOUT IRVING BERLIN

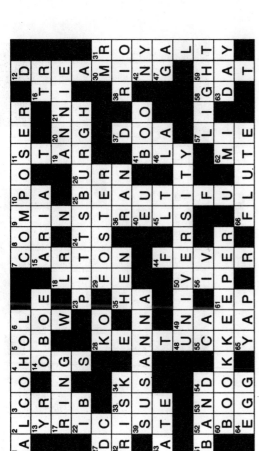

SOLUTIONS

9. ALL ABOUT GEORGE GERSHWIN

10. ALL ABOUT AARON COPLAND

11. ALL ABOUT LEONARD BERNSTEIN

12. ALL ABOUT JOHN LENNON AND PAUL McCARTNEY

SOLUTIONS

13. ALL ABOUT CAROLE KING

14. ALL ABOUT TYPES OF COMPOSITIONS

15. ALL ABOUT CLASSIC FOLK IDIOM COMPOSERS

16. ALL ABOUT CLASSIC JAZZ COMPOSERS

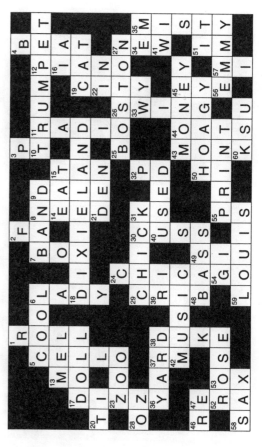

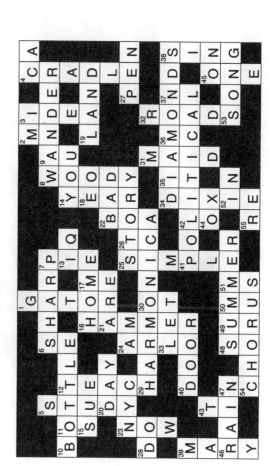

SOLUTIONS

17. ALL ABOUT CLASSIC COUNTRY COMPOSERS

18. ALL ABOUT CLASSIC BROADWAY COMPOSERS

19. ALL ABOUT CLASSIC ROCK COMPOSERS

20. ALL ABOUT CLASSIC MOTOWN COMPOSERS

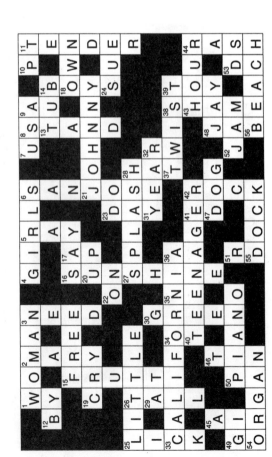

BIBLIOGRAPHY

Abraham, Gerald. THE CONCISE OXFORD HISTORY OF MUSIC.
New York: Oxford University Press, 1985.

Apel, Willi. HARVARD DICTIONARY OF MUSIC.
Cambridge: Harvard University Press, 1968.

Belz, Carl. THE STORY OF ROCK.
New York: Harper & Row, 1972.

Chase, Gilbert. AMERICA'S MUSIC.
New York: McGraw-Hill Book Company, 1966.

Earhart, Will and Birge, Edward. SONGS OF STEPHEN FOSTER.
Pittsburgh: University of Pittsburgh Press, 1968.

Engel, Lehman. THE AMERICAN MUSICAL THEATRE.
New York: Macmillan Publishing Company, Inc., 1967.

Gridley, Mark. JAZZ STYLES.
Englewood Cliffs, New Jersey: Prentice-Hall, Inc., 1978.

Hill, Thomas. COUNTRY MUSIC.
New York: Franklin Watts, 1978.

Horstman, Dorothy. SING YOUR HEART OUT, COUNTRY BOY.
New York: E.P. Dutton & Company, Inc., 1975.

THE MOTOWN ERA.
Miami: CPP/Belwin, Inc., 1971.

Nite, Norm. ROCK ON. Vol. I.
New York: Thomas Y. Crowell Company, 1974.

Nite, Norm. ROCK ON. Vol. II.
New York: Thomas Y. Crowell Company, 1978.

Okun, Milton. SOMETHING TO SING ABOUT.
New York: Macmillan Publishing Company, Inc., 1968.

Roxon, Lillian. ROCK ENCYCLOPEDIA.
New York: Grosset and Dunlap, 1969.

Rublowsky, John. MUSIC IN AMERICA.
New York: Crowell-Collier Press, 1967.

Scholes, Percy. THE OXFORD JUNIOR COMPANION TO MUSIC.
New York: Oxford University Press, 1979.

Stearns, Marshall. THE STORY OF JAZZ.
New York: Oxford University Press, 1958.

Waller, Don. THE MOTOWN STORY.
New York: Charles Scribner's Sons, 1985.

Westrup, J.A. and Harrison, F.L. THE NEW COLLEGE ENCYCLOPEDIA OF MUSIC.
New York: W.W. Norton & Company, Inc., 1960.